GRAPHIC PREHISTORIC ANIMALS

SABRE-TOOTHED TIGER

SMILODON

ILLUSTRATED BY ALESSANDRO POLUZZI

W
FRANKLIN WATTS
LONDON · SYDNEY

Franklin Watts
This edition published in the UK in 2018 by The Watts Publishing Group

Designed and illustrated by David West

ISBN 9781445159072 (hardback)
ISBN 9781445159065 (paperback)

Printed in Malaysia

Franklin Watts
An imprint of
Hachette Children's Group
Part of The Watts Publishing Group
Carmelite House
50 Victoria Embankment
London EC4Y 0DZ

An Hachette UK company.
www.hachette.co.uk

www.franklinwatts.co.uk

GRAPHIC PREHISTORIC ANIMALS SABRE-TOOTHED TIGER
was produced for Franklin Watts by
David West Children's Books, 6 Princeton Court, 55 Felsham Road, London SW15 1AZ

CONTENTS

Words in **bold** can be found in the glossary.

WHAT IS A SABRE-TOOTHED TIGER?

SMILODON MEANS 'BLADE TOOTH'

Sabre-tooths lived around 2.5 million to 10,000 years ago, during the **Pleistocene period**. **Fossils** of their skeletons have been found in North America and South America (see page 22).

It had a pair of very long **canine** teeth that curved like a sabre sword.

Its shoulders, front legs and neck were massively powerful – much stronger than a modern-day lion.

Although slightly smaller, it was twice as heavy as a lion.

Its jaws could open twice as wide as a lion's.

Its short tail shows it might not have chased its prey over long distances in the way a lion does.

SMILODON FATALIS (DEADLY) MEASURED 1.74 METRES LONG AND ONE METRE HIGH AT THE SHOULDER. IT WEIGHED 281 KILOGRAMMES.

It had strong, short back legs for jumping.

Its powerful claws could be pulled in and held inside its large paws.

This would be a sabre-toothed tiger and you.

SABRE-TOOTHED TIGER FACTS

During the last big ice age, camels, giant bison and huge mammoths roamed all across North America. These massive **herbivores** were preyed on by powerful **carnivores,** such as big cats, wolves and giant bears. Of all these mega carnivores, the strong sabre-tooth, with its fearsome fangs, was the best equipped to ambush and kill big game quickly.

Smilodon's dagger-like canines measured 17.8 centimetres long. They were saw–toothed on both edges to slice through flesh easily. Strong when pulled from front to back, they were surprisingly **fragile** if pulled from side to side and could snap. A sabre-tooth had to be careful how it caught its prey.

Smilodon had curved sabre teeth to slide in and out of flesh for a killing blow…

…front teeth for carving

…and side teeth for biting off lumps of flesh for swallowing.

It is thought sabre-tooths might have cared for sick or injured members of their group, like African lions do today.

WHAT IS NOW CALIFORNIA, 30,000 YEARS AGO.

SHEAR TOOTH, THE **ALPHA MALE** OF A GROUP OF SABRE-TOOTHS, WATCHES AS HIS FEMALES CREEP TOWARDS A GIANT BISON THAT HAS STRAYED TOO CLOSE TO THE TREES.

THEY NEED TO GET WITHIN STRIKING DISTANCE. IF THE PREY STARTS TO RUN, IT COULD BE IMPOSSIBLE TO CATCH.

FOR NOW THE YOUNG BISON DOESN'T KNOW THE STALKERS ARE WATCHING.

SHEAR TOOTH LOST HALF OF ONE OF HIS HUGE CANINE TEETH IN A STRUGGLE WITH A MAMMOTH, BUT HE CAN SURVIVE WITHOUT IT. THE FEMALES DO THE HUNTING FOR HIM.

THE LONG GRASS AND SHRUBS GIVE EXCELLENT COVER FOR THE AMBUSH. TWO FEMALES CLOSE IN. THE BISON'S FINAL MOMENTS APPROACH.

ANOTHER FEMALE LEAPS AT THE BISON AND HOLDS IT IN A DEATH GRIP. USING HER IMMENSE UPPER BODY STRENGTH SHE WRESTLES IT DOWN TO THE GROUND.

MUWHEEE!

THE OTHER FEMALE POUNCES, THIS TIME HOOKING HER **SWORD**-LIKE CLAWS FIRMLY INTO FLESH.

GRAAAAGH!

THE BISON IS DRAGGED TO THE GROUND.

A THIRD FEMALE EMERGES FROM THE GRASS. SHE WAS WAITING FOR HER MOMENT TO ACT.

GRAAAAGH!

MWHEEEEEEEEEEEEEEE

CAREFULLY POSITIONING HERSELF IN FRONT OF THE STRUGGLING BISON'S THROAT...

...SHE PLUNGES IN HER CANINES AND BITES BACK.

GRRRRR

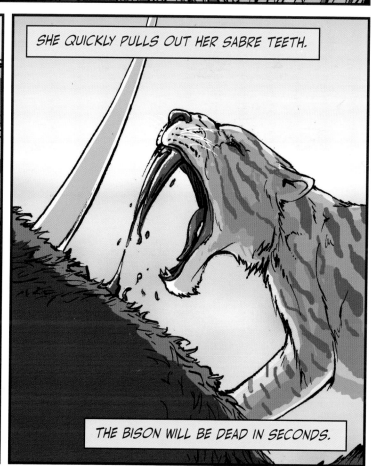

SHE QUICKLY PULLS OUT HER SABRE TEETH.

THE BISON WILL BE DEAD IN SECONDS.

ROARS FROM THE FEMALES DRAW THE FAMILY GROUP IN TO FEED. SPACE IS MADE FOR SHEAR TOOTH TO TAKE HIS PICK FROM THE BEST PARTS OF THE **CARCASS**.

REEOW!

GROUAAAAGH!

THEY EAT ONLY THE SOFTEST BODY PARTS. THE CATS' SABRE TEETH ARE TOO FRAGILE TO RISK BITING ON BONE.

THEY MUST EAT QUICKLY. THE STRONG SMELL OF BLOOD FROM THE KILL IS ATTRACTING THE ATTENTION...

...OF OTHERS.

SNORT-SNUFFLE

GRRRRRRR!

A GIANT SHORT-FACED BEAR BURSTS FROM THE TREES, SCENTING THE KILL SITE. IT RISES TO ITS FULL HEIGHT AND BELLOWS ITS CLAIM TO THE KILL.

BROUUHAAAA!

THE HUGE BEAR NOW HAS THE ADVANTAGE. THE SABRE-TOOTHS DARE NOT RISK THEIR TEETH BY BITING IT AND THEIR PAWS ARE NO MATCH FOR THE BEAR'S FEARSOME CLAWS.

ALL THE TIGERS BUT SHEAR TOOTH BACK OFF. STILL FEEDING, HE ROARS IN REPLY...

GRAAAAAAA!

...BUT IS SUDDENLY DISTRACTED.

ANOTHER MALE SABRE-TOOTH HAS APPEARED BEYOND THE BEAR.

GROARR!

THE BEAR SUDDENLY SWIPES AT SHEAR TOOTH, BATTING HIM SIDEWAYS.

RARGH!

SCRITCH!

AROUUUUUGH!

SHEAR TOOTH IS WOUNDED. HE LIMPS AWAY AFTER HIS GROUP AS BIRDS CIRCLE, WAITING FOR THE BEAR TO FINISH WITH THE BISON.

THE STRANGE MALE, MARKED WITH A DISTINCTIVE WHITE FLASH ACROSS HIS FACE, BOUNDS PAST SHEAR TOOTH TO GET AHEAD OF HIM.

HE BLOCKS SHEAR TOOTH'S ROUTE TO HIS GROUP AND ROARS A CHALLENGE.

ROAAAARRR!

SOME OF SHEAR TOOTH'S RIBS ARE CRACKED AND HIS LEG IS DAMAGED. HE CAN'T FIGHT THIS RIVAL. HE TURNS AWAY.

ROAAAR!

WHITE FLASH APPROACHES THE FEMALES. THEY SNARL AT HIM TO KEEP HIS DISTANCE. THEY WILL NOT ACCEPT HIM UNTIL THE CUBS FATHERED BY SHEAR TOOTH HAVE GROWN.

ROAAAR!

REEEE!

IF HE GETS CLOSE TO THE CUBS HE MIGHT EAT THEM.

WEEKS LATER, ALTHOUGH HIS WOUNDS ARE SLOWLY HEALING, SHEAR TOOTH IS IN WORSE SHAPE.

HE HAS BECOME AN UNDERWEIGHT WANDERER WHO IS CONSTANTLY HUNGRY. ALTHOUGH WARM, THE WEATHER HAS BEEN WET AND SHEAR TOOTH CANNOT FIND ENOUGH FOOD.

APPROACHING A CAMEL KILLED BY A PRIDE OF AMERICAN LIONS, HE WAS DRIVEN OFF BY THE ALPHA MALE. A PACK OF DIRE WOLVES WERE WAITING IN THE WINGS, READY TO TAKE OVER ONCE THE LIONS HAD FINISHED.

RAAAAGH!

SHEAR TOOTH HAD TO FIGHT WITH A VULTURE-LIKE TERATORN FOR THE MORSELS THE WOLVES LEFT BEHIND.

14

SMALLER GAME, LIKE THE DWARF PRONGHORN, ARE PLENTIFUL, BUT THE SABRE-TOOTH IS NOT BUILT FOR HIGH-SPEED CHASES.

THE SMALLEST PREY, LIKE RABBITS AND PECCARIES, ARE NOT A BIG MEAL AND ARE HARD TO EAT WITH OVERSIZED CANINES.

GRAAANYAAAGH!

THE TIGER'S OUTLOOK IS BLEAK.

EARLY ONE EVENING WHILE SEARCHING FOR WATER, SHEAR TOOTH'S EARS PICK UP THE DISTANT SOUND OF AN ANIMAL CRYING IN DISTRESS.

REEW! REEW! REEE

HE HEADS TOWARDS THE DIRECTION OF THE NOISE. A TRAPPED OR WOUNDED ANIMAL MIGHT MEAN AN EASY MEAL.

REEW! REEW! REEW! REEW! REEW!

A COLUMBIAN MAMMOTH LIES STRANDED IN THE MIDDLE OF A SHALLOW, BOGGY POND.

IT HAD BEEN TRYING TO REACH A GROUP OF YOUNG TREES IN THE MIDDLE OF THE WATER.

BRUUUAAACH! REEW! REEW! REEW! REEW! REEW!

AS IT WADED OUT, ITS FEET SUNK INTO THE BLACK *TAR* THAT BUBBLED JUST BELOW THE SURFACE.

SLOP!

THE TAR WORKED JUST LIKE GLUE.

BRUUAAAAGH!

SHEAR TOOTH DOESN'T KNOW THAT THE POND IS A HIDDEN DEATH TRAP. THE MAMMOTH'S CRIES GET FAINTER AS IT BECOMES EXHAUSTED.

APART FROM A LURKING BOBCAT, THE SABRE-TOOTH IS THE ONLY MAJOR **PREDATOR** ON THE SCENE.

SHEAR TOOTH REACHES OUT A PAW TO ENTER THE BOG WHEN...

RAAAAGH!

WHITE FLASH STANDS WITH THE SABRE-TOOTH CLAN. THEY HAD HEARD THE MAMMOTH'S CRIES TOO.

RAAAAGH!

GROOUUGH!

HE SNAPS AT SHEAR TOOTH TO BACK AWAY.

RAAAAGH!

THIS PREY WILL BE HIS TO CLAIM.

ROAAAR!

THE FEMALES AND CUBS LOOK ON AS WHITE FLASH ENTERS THE WATER.

GRRRRRRRRR!

HIS POWERFUL LEGS TAKE HIM HALF WAY TO THE MAMMOTH...

...BUT NO FARTHER.

RAAAAGH.?

HIS FEET ARE CLAMPED FIRMLY IN *ASPHALT*. THIS *TAR SEEP* WILL BE HIS TOMB.

ROOOOOOOOO...

19

SHEAR TOOTH RETURNS TO THE WATER'S EDGE. HE SNAPS AT THE FEMALES TO GET BACK.

GRAAAGH!

GRRRR!

GRRRR!

ZZZZZT

A WHOLE MAMMOTH IS TOO GOOD TO RESIST.

AGAIN HE PREPARES TO ENTER THE POND.

AWROOOUGH!
AWROOOUGH!

A NOISE FROM THE TREE LINE, GETTING LOUDER AND LOUDER, MAKES HIM HESITATE.

A HUGE PACK OF **MARAUDING** DIRE WOLVES ADVANCES TOWARDS THE SABRE-TOOTHS.

WHILE THE BOLDEST WOLVES BARK AT THE SABRE-TOOTHS, THEIR PACK MATES RUSH INTO THE WATER.

AWROOOUGH!

HEAVILY OUTNUMBERED, THE CLAN RETREATS WITH SHEAR TOOTH CLOSE BEHIND.

AWROOOOOOO

THE FEMALE GROUP NOW HAS NO MALE. THE FEMALES MIGHT MAKE SPACE FOR SHEAR TOOTH AT THE NEXT KILL. THEN THEY MIGHT LET HIM HEAD THEIR GROUP ONCE MORE.

FOSSIL FINDS

WE CAN GET A GOOD IDEA OF WHAT **ANCIENT ANIMALS** MAY HAVE LOOKED LIKE FROM THEIR FOSSILS. FOSSILS ARE FORMED WHEN THE HARD PARTS OF AN ANIMAL OR PLANT BECOME BURIED AND THEN TURN TO ROCK OVER MILLIONS OF YEARS.

The largest known sabre-toothed tiger, *Smilodon populator* (destroyer), lived in South America. Its sabres were an amazing 30 centimetres long. The La Brea Tar Pits in Los Angeles have yielded the most fossil finds of the sabre-tooth. Many show healed injuries and some have broken teeth. Hunting big game was rough work.

Smilodon populator

Both the North and South American sabre-tooths became extinct at the end of the ice age, along with the giant bear and the American lion. The warming climate may have reduced the rich grasslands, causing the big game to slowly disappear. Unlike coyotes or wolves, sabre-tooths were not adapted to hunt anything but large, slow-moving animals. They were also poor scavengers. Their heavy build and huge sabres were their undoing.

Smilodon fatalis

ANIMAL GALLERY

All of these **animals** appear in the story.

flat-headed peccary
Platygonus compressus
Length: 90 centimetres
*A small mammal similar to a
modern-day wild pig*

dire wolf
Canis dirus
Length: 1.8 metres
*Like a modern-day timber wolf
but much heavier*

American lion
Panthera atrox
Length: 3 metres
*Like an African lion but with
longer, stronger legs*

teratorn
Teratornis merriami
Wingspan: 4 metres
*A large, condor-like predatory bird with a sharp,
hooked bill for ripping flesh*

giant short-faced bear
Arctodus simus
Standing height: 6–8 metres
*The largest bear ever found, it had long legs
and huge bone-crushing jaws.*

Columbian mammoth
Mammuthus columbi
Overall length including tusks: 8.7 metres
A primitive elephant with long spiralled tusks

giant bison
Bison latifrons
Length: 4.6 metres
Larger and heavier than modern-day bison

GLOSSARY

alpha male the highest-ranking member of a group of social animals, such as lions, wolves and dogs

asphalt an oily mixture of tar and sand

canine a pointed tooth between the front teeth and cheek teeth of a mammal, enlarged for flesh-tearing in meat eaters

carcass the rotting body of a dead animal

carnivore a meat-eating animal

fossils the remains of living things which have turned to rock

fragile easily broken

herbivore a plant-eating animal

marauding roaming with the intention to attack

Pleistocene period the time between 1,640,000 to 10,000 years ago, marked by a series of great ice ages

predator an animal that naturally preys on others

tar a dark brown or black oily liquid

tar seep a sticky pool of oil that bubbles up from the ground

INDEX